BOTTLED ON THE ESTATE

THE WINE BUFFS
OF
BURGUNDY

12,5 % Vol.  750 ml

Artwork
CARRÈRE

Story
RICHEZ ET CAZENOVE

Coloring
ALEXANDRE AMOURIQ & MIRABELLE

Translation
JOE JOHNSON

BAMBOO
ÉDITION

© 2013 BAMBOO ÉDITION

116, rue des Jonchères - BP 3
71012 CHARNAY-LÈS-MÂCON cedex
Tél. 03 85 34 99 09 - Fax 03 85 34 47 55
Site Web : www.bamboo.fr
E-mail : bamboo@bamboo.fr

Dépôt légal : juin 2014
ISBN : 978-2-8189-3196-7

Printed in France

MÂCON-VERZÉ AND PIZZA CRUSTS

AFTER MY MÂCON-VERZÉ, LET ME SUGGEST TASTING MY "CHEMIN BLANC" MÂCON-VERZÉ.

WE HAVE A FINE, COMPLEX SMELL, WITH AROMAS OF WHITE PEACHES, PEARS, AND MIMOSA BLOOMS. A POWERFUL TASTE, WITH A LOVELY ACIDITY.

EXCELLENT, MISTER MAILLET. THIS WINE WILL BE AWESOME WITH PIZZA!

STOP! YOU'VE GOT IT ALL WRONG!

WITH THIS NECTAR, YOU NEED SOME TRUFFLE-FLAVORED RISOTTO OR SOME SCALLOPS WITH SUPREME SAUCE! NOT SOME STUPID PIZZA!

AND WITH A GRILLED HAM AND CHEESE SANDWICH? IT WOULDN'T BE BAD WITH A GRILLED HAM AND CHEESE.

OH, COME ON, WE'RE TALKING ABOUT A SUPERIOR, GASTRONOMICAL WINE WITH A LONG POTENTIAL FOR AGING!

AT WORST, DRINK IT WITH TURBOT IN PUFF PASTRY OR WITH SOME TRUFFLE-INFUSED MASHED POTATOES!

OR WITH A NICE, LITTLE SHISH KEBAB.

GOOD JOB, TERRY!

WHO WANTS A LITTLE MORE "CHEMIN BLANC" WITH HIS SCALLOPS?

GRRMMBBLL–PIZZA! KEBABS! GRILLED HAM AND CHEESE!!! AND WHAT ELSE??? I'LL MAKE THAT PUFF-PASTRY TURBOT MYSELF!!!

16

TASTE TESTS

AHHH – THE PLEASURE OF STROLLS IN BURGUNDY.

I DIDN'T KNOW THIS AREA!

IT'S REALLY CUTE!

WE DISCOVER A WINERY AND STOP TO SAMPLE ITS WARES.

SO, MY BEAUNE VINTAGE?

WELL, IT DOES ITS NAME HONOR.

ANOTHER ONE! DO WE STOP?

PASSING BY ONE PLACE-NAME, WE FIND ANOTHER ONE JUST AS NICE.

LET'S STOP!

CAVE

WINE TASTINGS–NEW AROMAS–NEW FLAVORS.

I GOTTA SAY THAT YOUR "NUITS-SAINT-GEORGES"–

PEOPLE ARE SO WELCOMING AND SO PROUD OF THEIR PRODUCTS–

DON'T MOVE! I'LL GO GET THE POUILLY 2009 FOR YOU!

WE QUICKLY GET INTO THE HABIT OF TASTING EVERYTHING.

VOUGEOT 1ST ROWTH! CHAMBOLLE-MUSGNY! CORTON– 'INTERES-TED?!

WE ARE!

OKAY, WE'LL TRY THAT ONE NOW!

A LITTLE TOO QUICKLY MAYBE.

LAKOUA

TRA

HMM, THESE RILLETTES–

AND THIS SALAMI.

3

A ROMANÉE-CONTI?!

YOU'RE TALKING A WHOLE BOTTLE OF ROMANÉE-CONTI?!

WOW! I'D NEVER SEEN AN ACTUAL ONE FOR REAL!

I'D BUY A WHOLE CASE, BUT REGINA REFUSES TO MORTGAGE THE HOUSE.

WOULD YOU LIKE TO COME TASTE THIS LITTLE JEWEL OF BURGUNDY AT MY HOME—

WE'D LIKE THAT A WHOLE LOT!

ON THE OTHER HAND, CONSIDERING THE THING'S PRICE, IT'D BE NICE OF YOU TO CONTRIBUTE—

NO WORRIES, MAURICE! OF COURSE!

YOU CAN COUNT ON US!

THAT EVENING.

SO THEN, YOU'RE UNCORKING IT?

NOW THAT YOU HAVE OUR MOUTHS WATERING.

WHAT?!

I BROUGHT SOME SALAMI! AND THOMAS GOT THE CHIPS!

YOU ALWAYS HAVE TO GET HUFFY!

YOU WANTED US TO CHIP IN, DIDN'T YOU?!

5

I SUGGEST YOU START BY TASTING A FIRST GROWTH RULLY! "LA PUCELLE."

SORRY? DID YOU SAY THE WORD FOR "VIRGIN"?

ABSOLUTELY. OUR "CLIMATS" HAVE EITHER NAMES WITH A RELIGIOUS ORIGIN, LIKE "NUITS-SAINT-GEORGE," OR A LINK WITH THE KIND OF SOIL AND SOMETIMES, LIKE WITH "LA VIRGIN-MAID," THEY'RE IMAGES.

A "CLIMAT"?

THAT THE BURGUNDIAN VERSION OF THE WORD FOR SOIL, AND WE HAVE OTHERS WITH A FUNNY RING TO 'EM, IF YOU'LL ALLOW ME.

FOR EXAMPLE, IN GIVRY, THERE'S A "CLIMAT" CALLED "HOOKE'S PLOT," MINUS THE "R."

THERE'S ALSO THE "CHICKADEES" AT NUITS-SAINT-GEORGES.

THE CHASSAGNE "SANCTIMONIOUS."

THE SAINT-AUBIN "MURGERS OF DOGTEETH"!

AND THE "STUPID SCHMUCK" AT SAVIGNY-LES-BEAUNE, ETC., ETC.

YOU'RE RIGHT! I GOT ONE HERE WITH AN IMAGE THAT HAS A REALLY STUPID NAME.

THAT WAS THE NAME OF HIS FAMILY WINERY, WASN'T IT?

OWWW.

BOO BOO.

CAVE

32

8

IT SEEMS VERY FRUITY TO ME, DOESN'T IT?

THAT'S THE CHARACTERISTIC OF A GOOD VOLNAY, IN FACT!

MEILLEUR CR 1992 MEDAILLE D'OR

BARRIQUE D'OR 1926

THE PINOT NOIR EXHALES AROMAS OF MORELLO CHERRIES ON OUR SOIL. YOU CAN FIND THOSE AROMAS IN A CHAMBERTIN, AS WELL.

HERE, MA'AM, OXYGENATE THE GLASS WELL BY TURNING IT AND TAKE A WHIFF!

AH YES! I SMELLED IT!

CRAZY! IT'S REALLY LIKE STICKING YOUR NOSE IN A BASKET OF CHERRIES!

LET'S GET SOME THEN!

COOL!

GIMME FIVE POUNDS, PLEASE. THE REALLY RED ONES!

CAVE

4

I DON'T REMEMBER IF I SAID SO, BUT YOU GOTTA HANG ONTO THE FIRST GROWTH GIVRY I GAVE YOU LAST WEEK.

YEAH! YOU EVEN TOLD ME I GOTTA KEEP IT FOR THREE YEARS, RIGHT?

AT A MINIMUM.

A BURGUNDY WINE IS EVEN BETTER ONCE IT'S FIVE YEARS OLD, ESPECIALLY A GIVRY!

IT MELTS INTO TIME—

IN THAT CASE, NO! I REFUSE!

WELL—UH—DO AS YOU LIKE.

I'M JUST GIVING YOU SOME ADVICE.

WELL, I HOPE YOU'RE REALLY SURE!

WELL YES! WHY DO YOU SAY THAT?

BECAUSE IT ALREADY SMELLS A LOT LESS GOOD IN ONLY A WEEK, SO I DON'T KNOW WHAT IT'LL BE LIKE IN THREE YEARS.

AND I DON'T DARE PICTURE FIVE YEARS.

IT JUST DOESN'T SEEM LIKELY.

14

OKAY, TODAY WE'RE GONNA DRINK A MEURSAULT CHARMES 2008, ONE OF THE LOVELIEST FIRST GROWTHS MEURSAULTS IN AN AWESOME YEAR FOR WHITE WINES.

LET'S JUST SAY WE WON'T BE DRINKING MUCH OF THIS VERY OFTEN!

YEAH, WE ABSOLUTELY HAVE TO MAKE SURE WE SAVOR THE WINE AS MUCH AS POSSIBLE!

I HAVE AN IDEA! SHAZAM!

SOME CHEAP SWILL JUST BEFORE! JUST TO GET OUR MOUTHS READY WITH THE WORST AND AFTERWARDS, MAKE WAY FOR THE BEST!

WOW! GOOD IDEA!

I'LL HAVE A SPOONFUL OF CASTOR OIL, A REMEDY MADE FROM COD LIVER THAT MY GRANDPARENTS USED TO USE. DEFINITELY YUCKY!

I'M JUST GONNA DRINK SOME VINEGAR!

MWOOOYUUUCK BWAAAH

AND YOU, TERRY? HOW ARE YOU GETTING READY?

I'M GOING TO THE DENTIST'S.

YIKES!

THE DRILL WILL GET YOUR MOUTH READY!

SO, DOC, HOW ABOUT TAKING OUT A MEURSAULT CHARMES 2008? I ALMOST DRANK SOME WITH SOME WHACKJOBS.

GOOD IDEA, TERRY, AND AFTERWARDS, WE'LL HAVE A 2010!

26

HMM—WHAT PHILIPPE CHARLOPIN IS DOING IS REALLY GOOD, HIS FIXIN "CLOS DE FIXEY," IS A PURE JOY!

YES, BUT FOR ME, THE GREATEST ONE WAS DENIS MORTET!

WHEN I TASTED HIS GEVREY-CHAMBERTIN "LAVAUX SAINT-JACQUES" 2004, HIS LAST VINTAGE—

—IT WAS A LITTLE AS THOUGH GOD HAD TALKED TO ME!

WHATEVER! THERE'S NO BETTER WINEMAKER THAN HENRI JAYER! HIS RICHEBOURG 1978 WAS THE MOST EXPENSE BOTTLE IN THE WORLD AT THE AUCTIONS!, AND I WON'T MENTION HIS LEGENDARY CROS PARANTOUX!

OOOH, THE INSINCERITY! ANNE-CLAUDE LEFLAIVE IS THE BEST! HER PULIGNYS ARE TO DIE FOR!

PFFF— YOU'RE BRINGING HER UP 'CAUSE SHE'S A GAL! YOU'RE DOING A WOMEN'S LIB NUMBER ON US!

AND JEAN-FRANÇOIS COCHE-DURY!

HAHAHA! NOBODY'S TALKING ABOUT JEAN-FRANÇOIS COCHE-DURY!

THERE ARE NO GREATER WHITES THAN HIS MEURSAULTS OR HIS CORTON-CHARLEMAGNE!

NO GREATER ONES!

THOSE PEOPLE WOULDN'T BE ANYTHING AND NEVER WOULD'VE BEEN ANYTHING WITHOUT SAMUEL HENSHALL.

! ?! !

ALL THE WINE-GROWERS YOU'VE NAMED OWE HIM EVERYTHING! HE'S THE GREATEST ONE.

AND WHO WAS THAT SAMUEL? CAN YOU TELL US, MISTER KNOW-IT-ALL?

THE INVENTOR OF THE CORKSCREW!

?!?!?

10

AND HERE'S YOUR WINE!

THANKS, FLORIANE.

TATSAAN TATSAN TATZA

TCHIC! TCHIC! TCHIC

SIR!

TATSAN

TATSAN

PLOP!

SERVED BY CANDLELIGHT UNTIL THE APPEARANCE OF A WHITE TRICKLE, AS IT SHOULD BE!

Hoooop

CLOC CLOC CLOC CLOC

WHAT'S GOING ON OVER THERE? WITH THE MUSIC AND ALL?

THEY ORDERED A MUSIGNY "COMTE DE VOGUE" 1929, A VERY, LOVELY BOTTLE.

IT'S NO EVERYDAY THING.

DO YOU ALWAYS MAKE THE SAME FUSS ABOUT IT IN HERE?

THIS MOMENT MUST REMAIN UNFORGETTABLE!

NOT JUST INSIDE EITHER! THE CHEF ALSO PARTICIPATES IN THE RITUAL—

—EVERY TIME WE SELL A BOTTLE AT THAT PRICE!

La Table de Chaintré

YEAAAH!

WOOHOO!

YEEHAWWW!

TAGADAP TAGADAP TAGADAP

23

INADVERTENT WINES

PEOPLE OFTEN BUY WINE FOR THE BIRTH OF A CHILD, FINE BURGUNDY WINES FOR AGING.

CLOS-DE-VOUGEOT, CHAMBERTIN, MUSIGNY-VINTAGES MEANT TO BRAVE THE YEARS—

THAT'S WHAT TERRY DID FOR AXEL'S BIRTH.

WITH THE IDEA OF OPENING THEM FOR THE GRAND OCCASIONS OF HIS SON'S LIFE: DRIVER'S LICENSE, GRADUATION AND, OF COURSE, HIS WEDDING.

BUT OBVIOUSLY, YOU SOMETIMES HAVE TO MAKE SURE THE WINE'S STILL SUITABLE FOR THE FUTURE EVENT.

THAT'S WHAT TERRY DID ON AXEL'S TWELFTH BIRTHDAY.

SO YOU WANT HIM TO DO HIS FIRST COMMUNION AND WEDDING AT THE SAME TIME?

AND HE WANTS MY TWELVE-YEAR OLD SON TO TAKE HIS DRIVING TEST AND GRADUATION TEST THIS MONTH! HE'S POSSESSED BY THE DEVIL, FATHER!

HMMMM, SO GOOD! THE WINE FROM HIS BIRTH—

24

THE WINE ROUTE

THE DISTINCTIVENESS OF BURGUNDY IS THAT THE SAME VINEYARD CAN HAVE VINES ON DIFFERENT PARCELS VERY FAR FROM ONE ANOTHER.

THIS ONE COMES FROM THE VINEYARD RIGHT HERE.

THIS PARCEL, MARSANNAY, IS JUST OVER A MILE FROM HERE.

AS FOR THIS FIXIN, IT'S LOCATED ABOUT FIVE MILES AWAY.

GLOUP!

THE GEVREY-CHAMBERTIN, EVEN FARTHER!

A VOSNE-ROMANÉE-

HIC!

HMM-TERRY-MAYBE IT'S TIME YOU STOPPED!

YOU'RE RIGHT, HIC, RESHINA-I'LL COME BACK!

WHAT DO YOU MEAN COME BACK?

HOC!

DON'T WORRY-I KNOW HIC THE WAY.

SO, HIC! FIRST, THE VOSNE-ROMANÉE.

NEXT-

11

17

WELCOME TO THE MERLIN WINERY. TO START OUR WINE-TASTING, I'LL PROPOSE TO YOU OUR POUILLY-FUISSÉ "CLOS DE QUARTS."

ANOTHER CLOS! CLEARLY, ALL THE BURGUNDY WINES ARE CALLED "CLOS" SOMETHING!

NOT ALL, FAR FROM IT, BUT IT'S TRUE THAT THE NOTION OF AN ENCLOSURE IS VERY PRESENT WITH US.

WE OWE THAT TO THE MONKS FROM THE ABBEY OF CÎTEAUX. THEY WERE THE FIRST ONES TO PUT UP WALLS AROUND THE VINEYARD PARCELS.

FOR EXAMPLE, THERE'S THE CLOS DE TART, WHICH IS COMPLETELY ENCLOSED WITH WALLS AND IS A MONOPOLY.

OR THE CLOS DES LAMBRAYS, IT'S ALL ONE PIECE, BUT IT'S A COLLECTION OF SEVERAL PARCELS AND PLACE-NAMES: THE BOUCHOTS, THE LARRÊTS, OR CLOS DES LAMBRAYS, THE MEIX-RENTIER.

THERE ARE ALSO SOME IMITATION CLOS LIKE THE CLOS DE LA ROCHE, OF WHICH THE CLOS DE TART IS PART. IT'S THE MOST IMPORTANT ONE IN SURFACE AREA, WITH SEVERAL PLACE-NAMES, BUT IT'S NOT AN ENCLOSURE.

THE CLOS DE VOUGEOT IS PARTICULARLY REMARKABLE BECAUSE ONE CANNOT IGNORE THAT MORE THAN 70 OWNERS SPLIT UP ITS 50 HECTARES AND 59 ARES!

AND THAT'S NOT TO MENTION—

OKAY, I GET IT. THE RED'S THERE, THERE'S OUR WHITE. DRINK UP!

YEAH!!!

27

19

A WORLD OF CHARDONNAY

REGINA, WOULD A LITTLE TRIP TO A CHARDONNAY WINERY MAKE YOU HAPPY?

WOOHOO! AND HOW!

ESPECIALLY SINCE I'VE READ THAT'S A GRAPE VARIETY FOUND IN NEW ZEALAND—

IN SOUTH AFRICA—

IN AUSTRALIA—

IN SOUTH AMERICA—

AND IN NORTH AMERICA, TOO.

WHERE DID YOU MAKE RESERVATIONS FOR?

WHERE THE WINE'S THE BEST!

AND THE LITTLE LADY DOESN'T WANT A LITTLE SIP?

WELCOME TO BURGUNDY!

SNIF!

ST VÉRAN
POMMARD

19

THAT'S "MONSIEUR" ROMANÉE-CONTI

?

WHAT'S GOING ON, REGINA? DID YOU GET ROBBED?

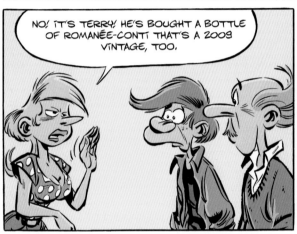

NO! IT'S TERRY! HE'S BOUGHT A BOTTLE OF ROMANÉE-CONTI THAT'S A 2009 VINTAGE, TOO.

WHAAAAA?! BUT THAT'S WORTH A FORTUNE!

THAT MUST BE WHY EVERYTHING'S EMPTY HERE. HE SOLD ALL THE FURNITURE TO GET IT.

NO WAY! NOT AT ALL!

HE WANTS TO BE ABLE TO ADMIRE IT IN THE BEST POSSIBLE CONDITIONS! $*@§§ TERRY!

CHAMO

22

SELECTIVE MEMORY

THIS MERCUREY IS NICE!

DO YOU REMEMBER US DRINKING THE SAME ONE AT YOUR SISTER'S WEDDING BETWEEN TWO BOTTLES OF CHEAP SWILL?

YOU TWO BLOW ME AWAY. YOU HAVE A PHENOMENAL MEMORY! I CAN BARELY REMEMBER THE COLOR OF THE WINE I KNOCKED DOWN YESTERDAY.

AND YOU REMEMBER ALL THE BOTTLES YOU'VE TASTED, WHERE, AND ON WHAT OCCASION.

AND HOW MUCH.

BAH! IT'S NOT COMPLICATED. FOR EXAMPLE, AT NOON, THE POUILLY-FUISSÉ AT VALETTE'S, I KNOW I HAD SOME ON THE EVENING WHEN I GOT MY DRIVER'S LICENSE.

WHICH YOU NEARLY LOST RIGHT AWAY.

AND THE SAINT-VÉRAN FROM THE DOMAINE DE LA CROIX SÉNAILLET ON SUNDAY, WE HAD SOME FOR OUR FIRST VALENTINE'S!

SURE DID!

INCREDIBLE! YOU REALLY DO REMEMBER EVERYTHING!

AHH!

WE'RE LIKE THAT!

WELL, THEY'VE FORGOTTEN US AGAIN.

WE SHOULD KEEP A BOTTLE OF WINE WITH US. THAT WAY, AT LEAST, THEY WOULDN'T FORGET ABOUT US ANYMORE.

GROUPE SCOLAIRE BOULARD

13

23

A NICE GLASS OF SAINT-VÉRAN "CROIX DE MONTCEAU"

SO, WHAT DO YOU THINK OF OUR SAINT-VÉRAN "CROIX DE MONTCEAU"?

UH–I'M JUST A NEWBIE.

WELL, AT MY FIRST WHIFF, I SMELL AROMAS OF WHITE FLOWERS AND BRIOCHE.

??

HMM, THE INITIAL TASTE IS STRONG AND VIVID!

!

BUT IT'S EVOLVING. IT'S AS THOUGH IT'S HEADING TOWARDS SLIGHTLY TOASTED NOTES.

AND YOU SENSE THAT, WHILE AGING, IT'LL EVOLVE TOWARDS EVEN MORE COMPLEX AROMAS.

?!?

????

WELL WHAT!? I'LL TASTE OUT OF YOUR GLASS INSTEAD, SINCE I DON'T HAVE ALL THAT IN MINE!!!

25

MAURICE, IT'S UNBELIEVABLE! DID YOU SEE WHAT THE WINE SHOP HAS STOCKED?

WHAT?

THEY HAVE A FIRST GROWTH LADOIX FROM CHRISTIAN PERRIN'S! A MAGNIFICENT RED, VERY BERRY-LIKE!

SO WHAT?

SO WHAT?!! IT'S REALLY GOOD!!! NOTHING GOES BETTER WITH A NICE PIECE OF MEAT—IT'S TOPS!

REALLY? WELL, IF YOU SAY SO.

SO? IS THAT GOOD FOR YOU?

IS WHAT?

YOU DIDN'T ASK HIM?

OOPS! I FORGOT!!!

WE'D LIKE TO INVITE YOU AND YOUR WIFE OVER TONIGHT.

WE'LL COOK SOME MEAT ON THE BARBECUE. DOES THAT WORK FOR YOU?

HERE, I BROUGHT A RED WINE!

OH! SOME LADOIX FROM PERRIN'S! WHAT A GOOD IDEA!

31

WHAT'S—?

HMM— GEVREY-CHAMBERTIN "LAVAUX SAINT-JACQUES"! AN AWESOME, AWESOME BOTTLE! YUM!

IS TODAY A SPECIAL DAY?

WELL, I DON'T KNOW. WHY DO YOU ASK?

OPENING SUCH A BOTTLE, SHE PROBABLY HAS SOME SURPRISE FOR YOU. IF I WERE YOU, I'D BUY A BOUQUET OF FLOWERS JUST IN CASE.

?!

HONEY! IT'S ME!

OOOOOOH! A BOUQUET! WHY?

BECAUSE IT'S A SPECIAL DAY, NO DOUBT, DON'T YOU THINK?

TWO QUESTIONS, HONEY! FIRST, HOW DID YOU KNOW IT WAS BOEUF BOURGUIGNON DAY?

AND SECOND, WHY DO YOU WANT ME TO SERVE IT TO YOU IN A GLASS?

28

EXPERT TEST

THERE'S NOTHING BETTER THAN A BLIND TASTE TEST TO SHARPEN THE PALATE.

WHOA, HE'S BROUGHT OUT THE BLACK GLASSES!

LET'S GO! FIRST WINE!

TO THE NOSE, IT EXHALES AROMAS OF BLACKBERRIES, BLUEBERRIES, AND PRUNE—A POMMARD!

YOU THINK SO? I'D HAVE BET ON A POUILLY.

AND THIS ONE?

HMM, THAT MAKES ME THINK OF A POUILLY.

NO! YOU CAN SMELL RED FRUITS AND SPICES: ALOXE-CORTON!

THE THIRD ONE HERE IS A POUILLY!

GOODNESS, ON THE BLIND TEST, YOU CAN SEE ONLY POUILLY-FUISSÉ. THAT'S NOT REALLY A RED, BUT A WHITE!

STILL, IT'S NOT EASY! WILL YOU GIVE US THE ANSWERS, PIANG?

WHAT ANSWERS?

SO WE'LL KNOW WHAT WE DRANK!

WHERE ARE THE BOTTLES?

I THREW 'EM AWAY, OTHERWISE IT'D BE TOO EASY!

LOOK AT THE GUY, I RECOGNIZE HIM, HE'S A JOURNALIST AT THE RVF*, HE'S A WINE TASTER WITHOUT EQUAL.

A TYPICAL SMELL OF CHARDONNAY—A FULL SOUTHERN EXPOSURE—A WINERY THAT HAS SUCCEEDED IN A BEAUTIFUL, ORGANIC MAKEOVER.

I SEE WHAT YOU MEAN, IT'S LIKE HE'S EVEN MORE THAN THAT, HE'S PRACTICALLY A WINE MEDIUM!

I CAN ALSO SEE THAT THE VINTNER HARVESTS ALL HIS GRAPES BY HAND,

IT'S LIKE HE HAS FLASHES AND SEES HOW THE WINE WAS PRODUCED—IMPRESSIVE!

THAT HE USES A WHEELBARROW TO BRING HIS GRAPE CLUSTERS INTO THE WINE PRESS—NEVERTHELESS, WE'RE HAVING A RAINY VINTAGE.

@*#%!! RAIN!!!

HMMM— I SEE,

I ALSO SEE A STEEP TERRAIN WHICH FAVORS THE FLOW OF RAIN WATER OVER A CLAYISH, CHALKY SOIL.

I ALSO SEE A SMALL, WOODEN FENCE, IS THAT RIGHT?

WELL? WAS HE RIGHT OR NOT?

IT'H A WALL, NOT A FENTHE, AT THE BOTTOM OF THE THLOPE—AND IT'TH DEFINITELY A RAINY VINTAGE.

'08

18

* THE FRENCH WINE REVIEW

MÂCON-BLANC IS A WINE OF RAPID EXPRESSION. IT HAS A BALANCE SITUATING IT BETWEEN A MERSAULT, SOMETIMES A LITTLE TOO ROUND, AND A CHABLIS, VERY CRISP AND A LITTLE POINTED.

GENTLE AND FRUITY WITH ITS AROMAS OF BLACKCURRANTS, RASPBERRIES, MORELLOS, CHERRIES, MERCUREY "PINOTES" WELL, MEANING, IT'S VERY REFLECTIVE OF THE EXPRESSION OF ITS GRAPE VARIETY, THE PINOT NOIR.

YOU'LL ENCOUNTER THESE VERY BEAUTIFUL AROMATIC EXPRESSIONS IN FIRST-GROWTH MARANGES OR GIVRYS, IF THEY'VE BEEN VINIFIED VERY WELL.

TO COME BACK TO THE WHITE WINE, THE MERSAULT IS A FLATTERING WINE, OPULENT, FULL-BODIED, A FINE, REGIONAL WINE!

BUT IF I WERE TO ADVISE YOU, GIVEN THAT THERE ARE A FEW WOMEN IN YOUR GROUP, I WOULD LET MYSELF DRAW YOUR ATTENTION TO THE VOLNAY.

IT'S PRODUCED TO THE SOUTHWEST OF BEAUNE. IT'S A FINE RED OF ESPECIALLY GREAT ELEGANCE.

UH-EXCUSE US.

YOU WOULDN'T HAVE SOME COFFEE INSTEAD?

A COUPLE OF CROISSANTS, TOO.

Le Clos de l'Abbaye
Chambres d'Hôtes

8

33

31

WHEN YOU'RE CRAZY ABOUT WINE, NOTHING'S WORSE THAN BEING DOWN TO THE LAST BOTTLE IN YOUR CELLAR FROM A BELOVED WINERY.

YOU ALREADY BROKE OUT IN A COLD SWEAT WHEN ONLY THREE WERE LEFT.

EACH OF THE REMAINING BOTTLES WOULD ONLY BE OPENED FOR A SPECIAL OCCASION, AN UNFORGETTABLE MEMORY, A GREAT MOMENT.

EVERY WINE-LOVER WILL SAY SO: WINE IS EMOTION.

AND WHEN A WINEMAKER HAS CAUSED SOME FOR YOU, AND YOU'RE DOWN TO ONE LAST BOTTLE, KNOWING YOU'LL EXPERIENCE THE VERY LAST EMOTION WITH IT—

OKAY! OKAY! I GET IT!

BUT FROM THAT TO BURYING EACH OF YOUR LAST BOTTLES IN THE YARD!

DON'T TALK SO LOUD, WOMAN! THIS IS A SANCTUARY HERE!!!

34

HERE YOU'RE AT A FAMILY WINERY, OUR FAMILY HAS BEEN LIVING IN VOSNE FOR GENERATIONS.

WE'RE STILL ONE OF THE RARE ONES TO WELCOME GUESTS TO THE WINERY, WE'RE KEEN ON KEEPING THIS CONTACT TO GET FEEDBACK ON OUR WINES.

THAT'S MUCH APPRECIATED, AND WHAT'S MORE, YOUR WINERY IS HIGHLY SPOKEN OF, WE'RE IMPATIENT TO DO SOME TASTING AND BUYING.

ESPECIALLY SINCE IT SEEMS HIS VOSNE-ROMANÉE ISN'T VERY EXPENSIVE.

WE'VE COMPLETELY TURNED TO ORGANICS, THE WINERY'S ENTIRE PRODUCTION IS BOTTLED.

WE DO A SPECIFIC VINTAGE FOR EACH PLACE-NAME, CALLED A "CLIMAT" IN BURGUNDY, FOR EACH OF OUR VILLAGES OF VOSNE APPELLATIONS.

ROMANÉE-

PSCHIT

YOU'RE A REAL PAIN, PIANG.

BOSS, HOW MUCH IS THE BURGUNDY TABLE WINE?

PROMO

x2

WHAT'S GOING ON WITH YOU, PIANG? I'VE NEVER SEEN YOU LET YOURSELF LOOK THIS PITIFUL?!?

WHISKY?! BEER?! GIN?! MARGARITA?!

NOT VERY PICKY!

SHAME ON YOU!

I CAN'T BELIEVE IT!? YOU DIDN'T EVEN TOUCH THE BOTTLE THAT WE GAVE YOU!?

SHELLING OUT FOR A ALOXE-CORTON WAS REALLY WORTH OUR TIME!

I CAN TELL OUR GIFT MADE YOU HAPPY!

NO—THAT AIN'T IT, MAU-HIC! BUT—I—I KNOW THAT—HIC! I—I DON'T LIKE TO WASTE—HIC!

MY BREATHALYZER!—HAS EXPIRED—HIC!—THIS—THIS EVENING—HIC! I SURE WASN'T GONNA—HIC!—USE IT—WITH—WITH A GOOD WINE—HIC!

7

CHABLIS, THE PRICE IS RIGHT

SO, THIERRY? EH? THIS LITTLE CHABLIS WASN'T WORTH THE TRIP?

CAVE
DÉGUSTATION

YEAH, IT'S NOT BAD—BUT I'LL GET YOU TO TASTE ONE OF MY BORDEAUX'S AND YOU'LL SEE THE DIFFERENCE!

PFF, I KNOW YOUR BORDEAUX'S! BURGUNDY WINES ARE BETTER, 'NO QUESTION ABOUT IT! WHAT'S MORE, THEY'RE MORE EXPENSIVE!

MONTÉE DE TONNERRE

WERE YOU DRINKING OR WHAT?! YOU FIND THE MOST EXPENSIVE WINES AMONG THE BORDEAUX'S! IT'S BEEN THAT WAY SINCE PREHISTORICAL TIMES!

BLA BLA BLA BLA BLA !!!

YOU DON'T KNOW ANYTHING ABOUT IT! BURGUNDY WINES ARE BETTER, BURGUNDY WINES ARE MORE EXPENSIVE!

AND THAT'S IT!

BORDEAUX !

BURGUNDY!

BORDEAUX !

BURGUNDY!

BORDEAUX !

TRiiiiiTT!

WELL, OKAY! YOU'RE RIGHT—BURGUNDY WINE COSTS MORE.

1

37

MY MOREY-SAINT-DENIS AND ME

WINE IS SOMETHING TERRIBLY CONVIVIAL.

FOR NOON, I'M UNCORKING A MOREY-SAINT-DENIS!

!

THAT'S GOOD, I INVITED THOMAS AND KAREN TO COME EAT WITH US.

HELLO, YOU WINE BUFFS!

AH, WELL, HERE THEY ARE!

WE RAN INTO MAURICE ON THE WAY, SO WE BROUGHT HIM, TOO!

THAT'S GOOD!

I'LL CALL PIANG. THAT WAY, WE'LL ALL BE HERE!

WHAT'S MORE, TERRY BROUGHT ONE OF HIS BEST BOTTLES OUT OF HIS CELLAR.

SPEAKING OF WHICH, WHERE'S TERRY?

?

WINE IS EVEN MORE CONVIVIAL WHEN YOU DRINK IT ALL BY YOURSELF.

WELL, HE WAS HERE.

NO IDEA!

DON'T KNOW!

?

29

38

THE WINE
BUFFS
OF
BURGUNDY

NOTEBOOK

BUBBLE,
BUBBLE...

In the beginning was the bubble. For, just as with comic books, the story of wine is born in bubbles. Those caused by the first fermentation of the grapes' sugar transforming into alcohol. But, before explaining the conception of wine, I propose continuing for you the parallel between two worlds which are closer than you might think.

Just as a comic book fan is waiting for his favorite artist's latest work, a wine lover impatiently awaits his favorite winemaker's latest vintage. And Burgundy is the ultimate wine-growing region for personifying wine. The notoriety of certain wine producers rivals that of famous pencilers. So much so that insiders don't ask for an appellation such as a Pouilly-Fuissé or a Pommard, but rather the winemaker's name followed by a vintage. And a vintage, for comic books, is like a volume, a part of a story.

Just as storyboards are necessarily used in comic books, boards are also used to make wine in casks. In that case, they're called "staves." And 23 staves, once assembled, form a "tonneau" or a cask. In Burgundy, they like to call it a "fût" or a "pièce." We leave the term "barrique" (barrel) for our friends in Bordeaux. A "pièce" of Burgundy wine represents about 300 bottles, which is about as many panels in a graphic novel.

Onomatopoeias, which give a rhythm to comic strip panels' action, recall the sound of wine rolling inside the mouth. This little music of wine is similar to the soundtrack contained in speech bubbles. The comic book bubble is similar to the label on the bottle, and the caption containing the narrative elements is, in fact, like the back label that gives information about food pairings or the wine producer's history. Conceiving a graphic novel takes time; producing a Burgundy wine takes between six months and two years, sometimes longer! So, to the rhythm of these pages along with an equal number of trips to the wine-cellar, I invite you to get a taste of Burgundy humor in speech balloons.

Guillaume Baroin

Bourgogne and its five wine-producing regions
La Bourgogne et ses cinq régions viticoles

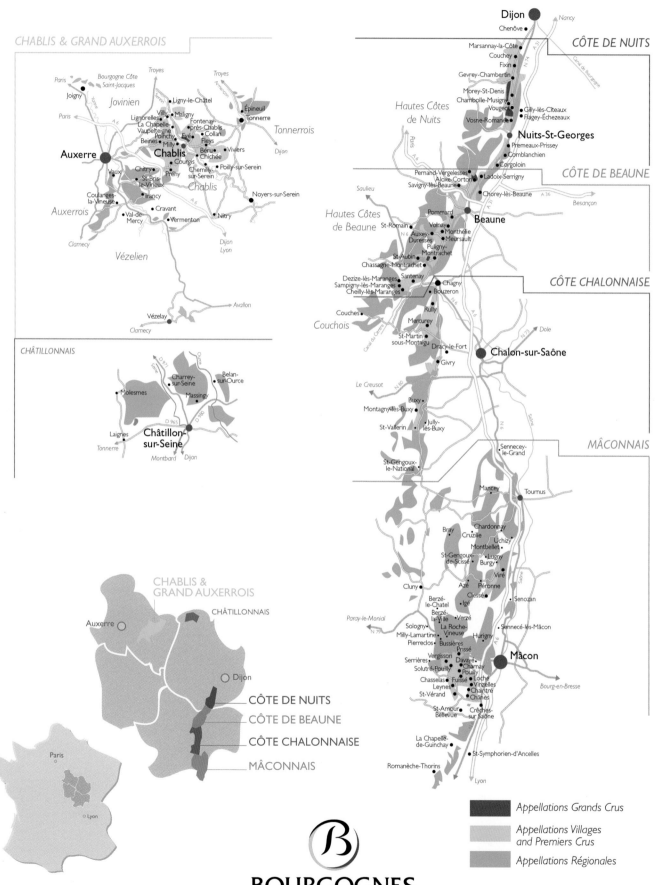

CHABLIS & GRAND AUXERROIS

Paris
Joigny
Jovinien
Bourgogne Côte Saint-Jacques
Troyes
Ligny-le-Châtel
Troyes
Épineuil
Tonnerre
Tonnerrois
Paris
Lignorelles
La Chapelle-Vaupelteigne
Poinchy
Beines
Milly
Villy
Maligny
Fontenay-près-Chablis
Collan
Fleys
Eyé
Bérru
Chichée
Viviers
Dijon
Auxerre
Chablis
Courgis
Chemilly-sur-Serein
Poilly-sur-Serein
Vaux
Chitry
St-Bris-le-Vineux
Préhy
Chablis
Noyers-sur-Serein
Coulanges-la-Vineuse
Irancy
Auxerrois
Val-de-Mercy
Cravant
Nitry
Clamecy
Vermenton
Dijon
Lyon
Vézelien
Avallon
Vézelay
Clamecy

CHÂTILLONNAIS
Charrey-sur-Seine
Belan-sur-Ource
Molesmes
Massingy
Laignes
Tonnerre
Châtillon-sur-Seine
Montbard
Dijon

Paris
Lyon

CHABLIS & GRAND AUXERROIS
CHÂTILLONNAIS
Auxerre
Dijon

CÔTE DE NUITS
CÔTE DE BEAUNE
CÔTE CHALONNAISE
MÂCONNAIS

Dijon
Nancy
Chenôve
Marsannay-la-Côte
CÔTE DE NUITS
Couchey
Fixin
Gevrey-Chambertin
Hautes Côtes de Nuits
Morey-St-Denis
Chambolle-Musigny
Vougeot
Gilly-lès-Cîteaux
Flagey-Échezeaux
Vosne-Romanée
Nuits-St-Georges
Premeaux-Prissey
Comblanchien
Corgoloin
CÔTE DE BEAUNE
Pernand-Vergelesses
Ladoix-Serrigny
Aloxe-Corton
Savigny-lès-Beaune
Chorey-lès-Beaune
Besançon
Hautes Côtes de Beaune
Pommard
Beaune
St-Romain
Volnay
Monthélie
Auxey-Duresses
Meursault
St-Aubin
Puligny-Montrachet
Chassagne-Montrachet
Santenay
Dezize-lès-Maranges
Chagny
CÔTE CHALONNAISE
Sampigny-lès-Maranges
Bouzeron
Cheilly-lès-Maranges
Couches
Rully
Mercurey
Couchois
St-Martin-sous-Montaigu
Dracy-le-Fort
Chalon-sur-Saône
Givry
Le Creusot
Buxy
Montagny-lès-Buxy
St-Vallerin
Jully-lès-Buxy
Sennecey-le-Grand
MÂCONNAIS
St-Gengoux-le-National
Mancey
Tournus
Bray
Chardonnay
Cruzille
Uchizy
Montbellet
St-Gengoux-de-Scissé
Lugny
Burgy
Viré
Cluny
Azé
Péronne
Clessé
Senozan
Berzé-le-Châtel
Igé
Berzé-la-Ville
Verzé
Sologny
La Roche-Vineuse
Hurigny
Sennecé-lès-Mâcon
Milly-Lamartine
Bussières
Pierreclos
Prissé
Vergisson
Davayé
Mâcon
Serrières
Charnay
Solutré-Pouilly
Pouilly
Loché
Bourg-en-Bresse
Chasselas
Fuissé
Vinzelles
Leynes
Chaintré
St-Vérand
Chânes
St-Amour-Bellevue
Crêches-sur-Saône
La Chapelle-de-Guinchay
St-Symphorien-d'Ancelles
Romanèche-Thorins
Lyon

Appellations Grands Crus
Appellations Villages and Premiers Crus
Appellations Régionales

BOURGOGNES

www.grandpavois.fr • 2014 Edition

GEOGRAPHY AND HISTORY

THE LOCATION AND A FEW KEY FIGURES

Burgundy's vineyards are divided into five wine-producing regions that, over an area of 143 miles from north to south, comprise its diversity. On some 69980 acres*, that is, 3% of French vineyards (which equals only 0.5% of the world's vineyards!), Burgundy is, with its 100 appellations, in the first national rank through its number of such designations. In a normal year, it produces some 200 million bottles, or 2 bottles out of every 10,000 in the world. Only a drop of wine, in other words, but what a drop—

*(surface area in 2011, BIVB figures)

GRAPE VARIETIES

In this wine-producing region with a semi-continental climate, the vintage is necessarily important. Thus, a year's climatology influences the grape's quality and, consequently, its final product. **The majority of Burgundy wines come from two grape varieties: Chardonnay for white wine (46%)* and Pinot Noir (36%) for red.** Depending on the appellation, they coexist with Gamay, the grape variety of Beaujolais (7,5%) and Aligoté (6%). A few other native varieties such as the Sauvignon (which became the appellation Saint-Bris in 2003), the Pinot Blanc, and the César round out the family (4,5%). Except for the Bourgogne Passe-Tout-Grains which results from a blend of a minimum of one third of Pinot Noir and the rest of Gamay, blends of grape varieties are prohibited.

TERROIR AND "CLIMATS"

The nature of the soil and subsoil from which the vine stock draws its nutrients passing through several geological stages constitutes the key to the terroir. The terroir is the foundation of classification of Burgundy appellations. This concept established by monks and wine-producers dates back to the 7th Century AD, to the moment of their creation of the first "clos."

Principally exposed on the south-south east, Burgundy's wine-producing slopes welcome the vines into their soil at an altitude between 600 and 1500ft. This diversity is made even more complex by a unique value showcased by the wine-growing region's founders: the notion of "climat."

And the "climate" in Burgundy is not just the local weather, even though, as with any occupation tied to the soil, it is essential. Climats are clearly delineated parcels of vines, which benefit from particular climatic, geological conditions. Combined with the work of the winemaker, they form a giant puzzle of 1, 247 pieces. For example, the climat can include

the mention of "Clos" when it's enclosed with walls. It is these climats which have shaped the landscape where men live. The first recognized climat is the one planted by the monks of the Abbey of Cîteaux in the 7th Century: the Clos de Bèze. Other no-less-famous ones like the Clos-Vougeot (red wine) or the Montrachet (white wine) have contributed to the reputation of Burgundy wines.

The Clos de Vougeot - Credit BIVB/DR

THE APPELLATIONS

Made official by the INAO* in 1935, Burgundy appellations are governed by a hierarchy created by history and the reputation of the wine coming from each parcel. One can envision it like a pyramid with four levels, whose base would be generic Burgundy wines and whose summit is the finest red and white vintages.

* Institut National des Appellations d'Origine

Grands crus or "Fine Vintages"
1.4% of total production
33 AOC
e.g. Charmes Chambertin, Montrachet

Premiers crus or "First Growth" wines
10.2% of total production
640 classic Climats classed as "Premiers crus"
e.g. Volnay 1er Cru, Santenots, Chablis 1er Cru, Montmains

Village Appellations
37.3% of total production
44 AOC
e.g. Mercurey, Pouilly-Fuissé

Regional Appellations
51.1% of total production
23 AOC
e.g. Bourgogne Rouge, Mâcon-Villages

Pyramid figures:
- 57% / 43%
- 44,9% / 55,1%
- 24,8% 0,2% / 75%
- 30% 1.5% 16.3% / 52.2%

Red wines **Rosé wines** Sparkling Burgundy wines White wines

Pyramid of appellations
Average production figures, 2007-2011

VINE AND VINIFICATION

October	November	December	January	February	March	April	May	June	July	August	September
Uprooting			Pruning		End of pruning	Soil removal from vine base	Graft planting	Fertilization	Shallow hoeing	Sundry caretaking	
Soil preparation			Pruning		Fertilizer spreading	Soil and root removal	Bud removal	Cluster trimming	Soil and root removal	Graft-root removal	Leaf removal
Pre-cutting			Pruning		Grafting	Cane wiring	Shoot tying			Winery equipment prep	
Prep pruning			Pruning			Shallow hoeing		Summer pruning			Grape harvest
Vine removal			Pruning			Cuttings planting	Anti-fungal and insecticide spraying				Grape harvest
Soil piling			Pruning			New plantings					Grape harvest
Soil replenishment			Pruning			Weeding			Trimming		Grape harvest

Table of vineyard activity in Burgundy

Marketed in vats since the beginning of the 19th Century, Burgundy wines are divided into three wine categories. As in many other French wine-producing regions, whites have overtaken red wines, with 61% of volume against 31% for reds, but also rosés. The remaining 8% have become sparkling wines since the creation of the appellation "crémant de Bourgogne" in 1975, even though in 1830 Alfred de Musset was already celebrating the effervescent Burgundy wine in his *Secret Thoughts of Raphael*.

Mythical fine vintages have marked both local history and also the international history of wines. Here's a list, necessarily limited, but not ranked. These wine varieties still serve as references, indeed yardsticks for producers the world over. Certain wines are monopolies (meaning they belong to one person), others are products of over 80 proprietors.

> PINOT NOIR GIVES OFF AROMAS OF MORELLO CHERRIES THROUGHOUT OUR LAND— YOU CAN ALSO FIND THESE AROMAS IN A CHAMBERTIN.

Pinot Noir version, ruby-colored

- ✔ **Chambertin** 28.29 hectares, including the 15.38 hectares of the Clos de Bèze planted in 640 A.D. That was Napoleon's favorite wine.

- ✔ **Clos-vougeot** 49.86 hectares and a name that rings "Burgundy."

- ✔ **Musigny** 10.70 hectares and a micro-parcel of Chardonnay of 0.66 hectare. Why be simple when you can be complicated.

- ✔ **Romanée-conti** only 1.80 hectare of legend, and the most expensive red wine in the world.

Chardonnay version, tinged with gold

- ✔ **Montrachet** On 7.99 hectares divided between Chassagne and Puligny. At the latter municipality, it takes on the particle. So there, it's named: "Le" Montrachet. A wine "to be savored on your knees with your head bared," according to Alexandre Dumas.

- ✔ **Bâtard-montrachet** The legitimate child of the hill, located at the foot of the Montrachet vintage, under which it spreads its 11.86 hectares.

- ✔ **Corton-charlemagne** 53.44 hectares spread over Ladoix-Serrigny, Aloxe-Corton, and Pernand-Vergelesses, a white-bearded emperor.

- ✔ **Les Clos** 26.43 hectares around Chablis, the spirit of the famous Burgundian "minerality."

Other "grands crus," 33 in total, form the summit of Burgundy wines. Which mustn't make you forget the diversity of the excellent first-growth wines which, when they are carefully turned to wine, are on a first-name basis with the grand crus in terms of quality. Depending on the appellation, the villages produce greater quantities of bottles. They are the handsome ambassadors of the Burgundy vineyards. As for their part, generic Burgundy wines comprise the majority of the bottles which, at less cost, offer a very good rapport of price and pleasure.

COMMERCIALIZATION AND TRADITION

SALES BY THE BOTTLE

In this gourmet region, the secular tradition of welcoming the client is combined with an art of living. If chance brings you to a winegrower's cellar or a merchant's wine-shop, you must know a few basic rules to benefit from this rare moment:

✔ **Take your time,** you're not at a supermarket. Here, we're tasting. And with your senses, please. After all, wine allows for the simultaneous stimulation of the eye, the nose, the mouth, but also hearing, starting with the sonorous "pop" of the cork. A walk down the cellar steps supposes an increase in your memories via your senses. So, leave plenty of time, between 1 and 2 hours, sometimes more, especially when the days are shorter like in winter.

✔ **Do your tasting in the mid-morning or the end of the afternoon,** your senses are at their sharpest before meals. And that will also give you an appetite.

✔ **Even if you are the group expert, don't showboat.** Your host knows what he's put in his bottle. He knows the dates of his vintages over several decades and how many new casks he's put down for his batch of wine. In short, he's the teacher, and you're his lucky students.

✔ **Let yourself be guided.** Your host knows in what order to have you sample his bottles. Enjoy the pleasure, exchange your sensations, you have a right to not like a wine batch or to prefer another one because "we all wear different pants." But avoid saying a particular wine isn't good: it may not be to your liking, but it may be to your wife's.

✔ **A Burgundian is curious about others,** he likes to know to whom he's selling his wines. If he finds common passions with you, you'll stand a better chance of being able to taste wine from your birth year, from a renowned vintage, or even a rare wine.

The Château du Clos de Vougeot - Credit: BIVB/IBANEZA

FRATERNAL ORDERS AND WINE FESTIVALS

Fraternal orders and wine festivals participate and maintain that spirit of sharing and also attempt to be one of transmission.

The most ancient and well-known of the wine fraternal orders is that of the Chevaliers of Tastevin whose motto "Never in vain, always in wine" well bespeaks them. Since 1934, it has made its goal the development of products of Burgundy and its folklore, its regional cuisine, but more especially its wines via two wine-tastings called "Tastevinage," wich occur within the walls of the Château du Clos de Vougeot. Other fraternal orders such as "Le Souverain Baillage" at Pommard, "Les Embrasseurs du Fin Goulout" at Montagny, or also "Les Piliers Chablisiens," are linked to the promotion of a single appellation.

Among the wine festivals, the sale of wines from the Hospices de Beaune is a highlight in local life. It takes place in Beaune every third weekend of November and puts the wines from Beaune's former almshouse up for auction. Profits from the sales go to the hospital of Beaune. Thus does wine come to the aid of the ill. On the last weekend of January, the Saint Vincent Tournante takes place. Since 1938, it has been welcoming fans of Burgundy wines coming from the world around to discover the solid, liquid charms of an appellation that changes every year.

Text by Guillaume Baroin, wine-writer and reporter
for *La Revue du Vin de France*

Acknowledgments:
Bureau Interprofessionnel des Vins de Bourgogne :
www.vins-bourgogne.fr

BOURGOGNES

GLOSSARY

Bâtonnage

The action of putting the lees* in suspension in order to "nourish" the wine.

Climat

Often confused with the "lieu-dit" or place-name (which is a cadastral notion), the word "climat" was coined in 1728 by the Abbé Claude Arnoux in his work on the wines of Burgundy. The association for the registration of the Burgundian vineyards' climats to the UNESCO World Heritage list defines it like this: "They are parcels of precisely delineated land, benefitting from specific climatic and geological conditions that, combined with human labor and "translated" by the two great Burgundian grape varieties, have given birth to an exceptional mosaic of ranked, world-renowned vintages." The names of the climats are varied and evoke history, geology, animals, plants, people, and various subjects that have brought a name to a "parcelle."*

Clos

A vineyard enclosed with walls of dry stones called "meurgers."*

Lees

They are the thick, liquid dregs that settle from the breakdown of wine. Maturation on lees, notably through "bâtonnage," allows the wine to be nourished.

Cabottes

Also called "cadoles," they're small, stone shelters made from "meurgers"* set amid the vines. Common to the Burgundian countryside, winegrowers of yore used them as shelters during bad weather.

Meurgers (or murgers)

Piles of flat, dry rocks, of lava origin, removed from the soil during pickaxing and plowing and put in piles. Shaped into low walls, they serve to demarcate a parcelle* of vines. The top of the meurgers is an assembly of flat rocks (generally lava) positioned diagonally (to better allow for rainwater runoff). When the wall encloses the vineyard, it makes the vineyard into a "clos."

Ouillette

A sort of watering can that lets one "ouiller," meaning to top off the wine casks after the evaporation of the wine in the cellar. Certain kinds have a candle attached to the end piece. If a gas has replaced the oxygen, the candle will go out. That's the signal for the winemaker to exit the cellar before he falls into an eternal sleep.

Ouvrée

This ancient agrarian measurement is based on the labor that a worker could do in a workday in the fields with hand tools. 24 ouvrées (that is 4.28 ares) make up a hectare.

Parcelle

Terrain planted with vines constituting a cadastral unit.

Pipette

A tool usually made of glass allowing one to remove wine from the interior of a cask or a vat.

Pièce

In the Burgundian dialect, it means a barrel of wine representing about 300 bottles. Its capacity is 228 liters versus 225 liters in Bordeaux. The difference of 3 liters is used for wine-tasting.

Cru

Derived from the word "crû" which means "croître" or "to grow." Therefore the first vintages are the "first to grow" which means they benefit along with the finest vintages from better conditions than do the other vines.